M.C. DIXON

The Adventures Of
LARRY
THE HOTDOG

COPYRIGHT 2021

ISBN: 979-8-4629-9660-3 (paperback)
ISBN: 978-1-7376964-0-7 (hardcover)

First Edition Book, Year 2021

Book cover design, illustration, editing, and interior layout by:

www.1000storybook.com

DEDICATION

To Larry, my grandfather, his father, and to my father after him. May your legacy live on for generations in the hearts and smiles of the children that read these books.

To the men and women that change the world every day in technical occupations around the world. I hope your inspiration fills the minds of young children for years to come.

Larry the Hot Dog was red with a brown bun. He never left his home at the restaurant without dressing up in his best ketchup and mustard.

Though Larry looked like a regular hot dog, he was no ordinary hot dog at all.

Larry was a magical hot dog. With the flip of the sign on the front door of the restaurant from "closed" to "open," he came back to life each day, bringing with him excitement for a new adventure!

Every day at lunchtime, Larry hopped into his brown paper sack and waited to see what adventure the day would bring.

Larry felt the bag wiggle and shake... he was on his way...

To have lunch with Karl the Construction Worker!

Larry could hear loud noises as they walked through Karl's construction site.

Larry took a peek out of his brown paper bag, and he couldn't believe what he saw!

Karl was building an amusement park.

Larry saw tall cranes that lifted tracks for a roller coaster high in the sky. There was a ferris wheel, and a carousel.

Karl used different materials to build with on the construction site, like wood, metal, and concrete.

Concrete is used for the hard foundation many of the rides and buildings are built on at the amusement park.

Wood is used for building kiosks, theaters, and even restaurants like Larry's!

Metal is used for siding, ride structures, and roofing.

Construction workers use tools of many different shapes and sizes to build.

Larry saw the tools Karl used to build with like, hammers, drills, and screwdrivers.

He saw orange cones and big yellow and red signs that gave special instructions for the workers.

Some signs say to "stop!"

Others say to use "caution" and "slow down."

Karl wore important safety gear, like an orange hard hat and bright yellow vest.

He also wore earplugs to protect his hearing from loud noises and safety glasses to shield his eyes from debris.

The safety gear protected Karl from getting hurt on the jobsite.

There were many trucks on the construction site.

A dump truck hauled dirt and material around the construction site.

Larry loved watching the big trucks dig.

His favorite truck was called an excavator.

Karl waved at other workers as he carried his brown bag to a special spot, a metal picnic table, for lunch.

The picnic table had a rectangle top with a long bench on each side.

Larry had a great day on his special adventure with Karl, but it was time for Larry to say farewell...

Larry is headed back to the restaurant to tell all his friends about his day on the amusement park construction site with Karl the Construction Worker.

Until another adventure!

ABOUT THE AUTHOR

M.C. Dixon is a Forensic Accountant by day, but by night she lets her mind wander to fictional worlds full of imaginary characters and fun adventures. She grew up in a four-generation family restaurant that is famous in the State of Alabama for none other than a hot dog. It was her time spent participating in the family business that helped to inspire these adventures.

She's married to a biomedical engineer who has a love for making people laugh and writing poetry. They have two children, G and Max. Together, as a family, they created Larry the Hot Dog.

CPSIA information can be obtained
at www.ICGtesting.com
Printed in the USA
BVHW020621261021
619845BV00007B/716